SOLVING CRIMES WITH
TRACE EVIDENCE

by Gary Jeffrey

illustrated by Peter Richardson

W
FRANKLIN WATTS
LONDON•SYDNEY

First published in 2009 by Franklin Watts

Franklin Watts
338 Euston Road
London NW1 3BH

Franklin Watts Australia
Level 17/207 Kent Street
Sydney, NSW 2000

A CIP catalogue record for this book is available from the British Library.

Dewey number: 363.2'562

ISBN: 978 0 7496 9243 8

Franklin Watts is a division of Hachette Children's Books,
an Hachette UK company.
www.hachette.co.uk

GRAPHIC FORENSIC SCIENCE: SOLVING CRIMES WITH TRACE EVIDENCE
produced for Franklin Watts by David West Children's Books, 7 Princeton Court, 55
Felsham Road, London SW15 1AZ

Designed and produced by
David West Children's Books

Editor: Gail Bushnell

Photo credits:
4&5, Andrei Tchernov; 6t, New York City Municipal Archives, 6m&b, National
Library of Medicine; 7t, David Waugh, 7m, National Library of Medicine; 44, sx70;
45, Chris Hutchison.

Printed in China

CONTENTS

FINDING EVIDENCE

The evidence found at a crime scene takes many forms. Sometimes it is so small it is barely visible. In the case of fingerprints, it is invisible until revealed by a process.

INVISIBLE PROOFS

Crime scene investigators (CSI) have well-developed methods to help them find evidence that may be present at a crime scene. In the UK the CSI are called scene of crime officers (SOCO).

Physical clues, such as traces of blood, fingerprints, fibres and other foreign material, are collected and sent to forensic science laboratories for study. (Forensics is a detailed examination of material that is of interest to the legal system.) The forensic workers will also compare the fingerprints, trace fibres and blood sample results with previously gathered examples held in national databases.

Often trace evidence will form a vital part of a police file, undermining a suspect's alibi or proving they had physical contact with a victim when they had denied it. In these cases, trace evidence is often referred to as a 'silent witness' - convicting criminals through what they left behind.

Blood is just one kind of trace evidence. CSIs have special chemicals that can reveal where blood has been even when it has been washed off. Blood itself will contain valuable information about who left it, through its DNA profile.

THE SILENT WITNESS

Early in the 20th century, scientist Dr Edmond Locard put forward a theory that every contact a person makes with another person or object leaves a trace. 'Locard's Principle' is the basis for much of forensic science today.

One of the early Bertillon *cards. The subject's measurements were written on the back.*

FINGERPRINTS

Locard's teacher, Alphonse Bertillon, invented the first criminal identification system in 1880. Based on the measurement of eleven bodily features, it was complicated to record. The police were attracted to the idea of using fingerprints alone, but didn't have a way of classifying them.

The problem was solved by an Englishman, Sir Edward Henry, in 1900, and by 1910 'The Henry System' was being used by police forces worldwide.

From 1892, the right thumbprint of Francisca Rojas, the first criminal to be identified by fingerprints.

The method of taking fingerprints has changed very little. The tools used are printer's ink, a roller, plate and paper.

The computer age has further revolutionised fingerprint detection, enabling the enhancement of partial prints and fast searching and matching through vast databases.

'The Henry system' divides fingerprints into groups based on pattern types. The three main patterns are called arches, whorls and loops.

UNDER THE MICROSCOPE

Microscopy was first used in a murder case as early as 1847, when minute pieces of a woman's scalp were found on a pistol butt. Human hair varies greatly around the body. Carpet and other fibres show distinctive characteristics when magnified. Unlike eyewitnesses, this physical evidence cannot lie or forget.

Each household's dust will have its own telltale mix of fibres, minerals and hairs.

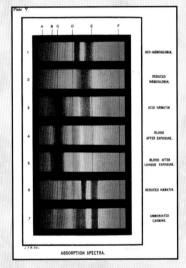

A chart showing the presence of toxins in a sample of blood tested using a spectroscope.

BLOOD AND OTHER BODILY FLUIDS

The study of blood evidence is called serology. In the late 1900s, blood could be tested for the presence of toxins using a spectroscope. A test could also show the presence of blood, and in 1901 blood types were discovered. However, a breakthrough came with the discovery of DNA in 1953.

DNA, a person's individual genetic 'blueprint', is present in every bodily cell. In 1987, the first criminal was identified and convicted using his DNA profile as evidence. The latest techniques can use material gathered from a single cell.

A DNA chart, marked to show the similarities between a sample collected at a crime scene and one taken from a suspect. The odds of two people in the USA having the same DNA are about 300 million to one.

THE DEPTFORD
PAINT SHOP MURDERS

LONDON, 25 MARCH 1905. CHIEF INSPECTOR FOX AND ASSISTANT COMMISSIONER MACNAUGHTEN HAVE BEEN CALLED TO THE SCENE OF A GHASTLY CRIME...

POOR FARROW. WHO COULD HAVE INFLICTED SUCH SAVAGERY?

MRS FARROW WAS FOUND UPSTAIRS BEATEN UNCONSCIOUS.

SHE'S BEEN TAKEN TO THE HOSPITAL.

MOVE ALONG PLEASE!

THE FARROWS RAN CHAPMAN'S OIL AND PAINT SHOP AT 34 DEPTFORD HIGH STREET.

THESE MASKS WERE FOUND ON THE FLOOR AND THERE'S AN EMPTY CASHBOX UNDER THE BED.

WE'LL NEED TO CHECK IT AGAINST THE VICTIM'S AND SERGEANT ATKINSON'S PRINTS.

DETECTIVE INSPECTOR COLLINS IS THE YARD'S CHIEF FINGERPRINT EXPERT.

THEN WE'LL NEED TO CHECK IT AGAINST THE RECORDS...

ONLY FOUR YEARS OLD, THE BUREAU ALREADY CONTAINS MORE THAN 80,000 SETS OF PRINTS.

THE BUREAU RECORDS COME UP BLANK. MEANWHILE, A DETECTIVE OVERHEARS SOMETHING IN A DEPTFORD TAVERN...

I HEARD IT WAS THE **STRATTON BROTHERS** THAT DID OLD FARROW.

YEAH, THEY'RE CAPABLE, ALL RIGHT!

KNOWN TO THE POLICE BUT NEVER ARRESTED, LOCAL ROGUES ALFRED AND ALBERT STRATTON ARE INVESTIGATED...

ALBERT STRATTON'S LANDLADY FOUND A BUNCH OF STOCKING MASKS UNDER HIS MATTRESS.

...AND ALFRED STRATTON'S GIRLFRIEND SAID HE'D BEEN OUT ALL NIGHT AND CAME BACK WITH A LOT OF MONEY...

THE FOLLOWING WEEK AT ANNE FARROW'S BEDSIDE...

SHE NEVER REGAINED CONSCIOUSNESS, SIR.

THEN WE'LL JUST HAVE TO ARREST THE STRATTONS WITH WHAT WE'VE GOT.

MAGISTRATES' COURT, TOWER HILL POLICE STATION...

THE GOSSIP-MONGERING OF AN OLD LADY AND THE WORD OF A FLOOZY! IS THAT ALL YOU HAVE, INSPECTOR FOX?

WE JUST NEED TO HOLD THEM FOR A FEW DAYS SO THAT WE CAN TAKE THEIR FINGERPRINTS.

AHH, DACTYLOSCOPY! I'D BE REALLY INTERESTED TO SEE THE NEWFANGLED METHOD. SUSPECTS WILL BE REMANDED FOR ONE WEEK!

HOLD STILL, PLEASE.

OOOH, THAT TICKLES!

THE PATTERNS OF RIDGED SKIN YOU CAN SEE WERE FORMED WHILE YOU WERE GROWING IN THE WOMB.

THEY ARE **UNIQUE** TO YOU ALONE. IN FACT, THEY ARE DIFFERENT EVEN IN IDENTICAL TWINS.

WHEN ONE TOUCHES A HARD SURFACE, THE OILS AND SWEAT ON OUR FINGERS WILL LEAVE A TRACE BEHIND.

IF PRESSED HARD ENOUGH, THIS **IMPRINT** WILL BE VERY CLEAR INDEED.

A CAREFUL DUSTING WITH INK DISPLAYS THE PRINT.

CLOSE EXAMINATION AND COMPARISON WITH A SUSPECT'S PRINT CAN REVEAL...

...EXACTLY **WHO** LEFT THE TRACE BEHIND.

ALFRED STRATTON'S FINGERPRINT IS ADMITTED INTO EVIDENCE...

HERE, WE HAVE LABELLED TWELVE POINTS OF AGREEMENT BETWEEN ALBERT STRATTON'S RIGHT THUMBPRINT AND THE PRINT REVEALED ON THE CASHBOX.

THERE IS NO WAY IT COULD HAVE BEEN LEFT BY ANY OTHER PERSON.

THE DEFENCE CALLS COLLINS'S FORMER TEACHER, CRIMINOLOGIST DR JOHN GARSTON, TO THE STAND.

THE FINGERPRINT CLASSIFICATION SYSTEM ADOPTED BY THE METROPOLITAN POLICE IS **FLAWED.**

I AM CERTAIN THAT THESE TWO PRINTS ARE *NOT* IN AGREEMENT!

HOWEVER, PROSECUTOR MUIR HAS AN ACE UP HIS SLEEVE...

I OFFER TWO LETTERS WRITTEN ON THE SAME DAY BY DR GARSTON OFFERING TO TESTIFY FOR THE PROSECUTION *OR* THE DEFENCE - DEPENDING ON WHO WOULD PAY HIM MORE!

BUT I AM AN INDEPENDENT WITNESS!

NO, DR GARSTON, UPON READING THESE I WOULD SAY THAT YOU ARE...

...A THOROUGHLY UNTRUSTWORTHY WITNESS! YOU ARE EXCUSED!

AFTER TWO HOURS OF DELIBERATION, THE JURY FINDS THE STRATTON BROTHERS GUILTY OF DOUBLE MURDER. THE JUDGE SENTENCES THEM TO HANG.

THIS WAS ALL YOUR IDEA!

WRENCH

HEY, GET HIM OFF ME!

THE CASE LAUNCHED THE SCIENCE OF FORENSIC DETECTION IN GREAT BRITAIN. FINGERPRINTING IS STILL AN IMPORTANT TOOL IN IDENTIFYING CRIMINALS.

THE END

I CALLED OUT BUT NO ONE REPLIED, SO I PAID IT NO ATTENTION. THEN THIS MORNING - THIS!

THE CORPSE IS TAKEN TO THE CITY MORGUE.

...WELL-ROTTED - DEAD ABOUT TWO WEEKS AND IT WAS STRANGULATION, WITH A ROPE OR STRAP.

ANY LEADS?

NOT YET, BUT WE'VE RULED OUT THE TENANTS - THEY ALL KNEW WHEN THE GATES WOULD BE LOCKED.

MEANWHILE, FRANCULESCU'S MEN HAVE CONDUCTED A SEARCH...

NOTHING! NO LINGERING STENCH OR STAINS. THE BODY HASN'T BEEN KEPT HERE.

NOT IN THE BUILDING, MAYBE, BUT WHAT ABOUT IN THE ROOF SPACE?

19

EVIDENTLY THERE WAS A **STRUGGLE**.

...BUT THESE ARE COARSE AND CUT, LIKE CHIN STUBBLE, AND THEY DON'T BELONG TO THE CORPSE.

THAT'S NOT ALL. I FOUND THIS ON THE VICTIM'S THIGH...

...A NUMBER FOUR SCRATCHED INTO THE FLESH POST-MORTEM.

THE NEWSPAPER BLOOD IS NOT FROM THE VICTIM AND THE DUST IS DIFFERENT FROM THE ATTIC DUST.

A REVENGE KILLING!

IT'S ORDINARY HOUSE DUST FROM A VERY DUSTY ROOM.

THE INVESTIGATION GRINDS TO A HALT. FRANCULESCU IS UNDER PRESSURE...

LOTS OF FORENSIC EVIDENCE BUT NO LEADS! I MUST BE **MISSING** SOMETHING!

HMM...THERE WERE A LOT OF BYSTANDERS WATCHING THAT DAY.

PETER KURTIN, THE VAMPIRE OF DUSSELDORF, USED TO LOITER AT THE SCENE OF HIS CRIMES. I WONDER...

FRANCULESCU HAS PHOTOS OF THE MALE ONLOOKERS ENLARGED. HE TELLS HIS SQUAD TO FIND OUT WHICH ONES HAVE RED HAIR.

WEEKS GO BY, UNTIL...

A CAFE OWNER RECOGNISED *THIS* MAN AS HAVING RED HAIR.

HE SAW HIM TALKING WITH **ANOTHER** REDHEADED MAN TWO DAYS BEFORE THE MURDER.

...AND LET ME GUESS - HE DOESN'T HAVE A NAME FOR HIM AND HE HASN'T SEEN HIM SINCE!

YES, BUT...WHERE ARE YOU GOING?

FOR SOME FRESH AIR!

FRANCULESCU GOES TO THE ROOF OF 55 AVENUE MAGUREANU.

THE QUESTION IS - HOW DID THE KILLER AND THE VICTIM GET INTO THE ATTIC?

I'VE CHECKED ALL AROUND THE ROOF AND THERE IS ONLY ONE OTHER BUILDING NEARBY.

WAIT A MINUTE...A FIT MAN COULD EASILY JUMP ACROSS THIS GAP.

WHO IS THE OWNER OF THAT HOUSE?

THE HOUSE IS OCCUPIED BY AN ARMY MAJOR.

OF COURSE I KNOW HIM. THAT'S BARDICA. HE USED TO BE MY BATMAN*.

*OFFICER'S SERVANT.

"HE WAS AWFUL, LAZY, DISHONEST. HE LEFT THE ARMY THREE WEEKS AGO AND QUITE HONESTLY I WAS GLAD TO SEE HIM GO."

"MAJOR MIHAIL, DID BARDICA LIVE IN THE SOUTH SIDE ATTIC ROOM?"

"WHY YES! HOW DID YOU KNOW?"

WHEN ALEXANDRU BARDICA IS FOUND AND CONFRONTED WITH THE EVIDENCE...

...HE MAKES A FULL CONFESSION.

HIS NAME WAS LADISLAS JURCA. HE USED TO BE MY ARMY BUDDY...

...SO THEY WERE CONSCRIPTS IN A GANG WITH TWO OTHER REDHEADS, COMMISSIONER.

"THEY CALLED THEMSELVES *THE FOUR MUSKETEERS*."

"WHEN JURCA WAS SUDDENLY PROMOTED HE GOT A KICK OUT OF ORDERING THE OTHER MEN AROUND - ENJOYED **HUMILIATING** THEM."

"IT WAS TOO MUCH FOR BARDICA. HIS FEELINGS OF FRIENDSHIP TURNED TO HATRED. HE VOWED TO GET REVENGE."

"HE WAS STILL MAD ABOUT IT WHEN HE WENT TO WORK FOR THE MAJOR."

"WHEN HE BROKE INTO THE ATTIC ROOMS LOOKING TO STEAL AND FOUND THE EMPTY PACKING CASE..."

"...IT GAVE HIM A WICKED IDEA..."

"WHEN I TOLD JURCA THAT THE PACKING CASE WAS FULL OF LOOT HE WANTED IN."

IT WAS EASY.

BARDICA IS GIVING EVIDENCE TO THE JUDGE.

"WHEN WE WERE IN THE ATTIC HE BENT FORWARD TO LIFT THE LID, AND..."

"HE FOUGHT BACK, BUT I WAS TOO STRONG FOR HIM."

WHY DID YOU WAIT TWO WEEKS TO REMOVE THE BODY?

I'D NAILED HIM IN TIGHTLY, BUT I WAS WORRIED THAT THE STINK WOULD EVENTUALLY LEAD THE POLICE TO MY ROOM.

SO ON MY LAST NIGHT OF DUTY I DECIDED TO DUMP HIM IN THE RIVER.

"I HAD TO DRAG HIM DOWN THE STAIRS, WHICH WOKE A WOMAN UP. LUCKILY FOR HER, SHE DIDN'T COME OUT."

WHO'S THERE?

"WHEN I FOUND THAT THE GATES WERE LOCKED I GAVE UP AND LEFT HIM FOR THE COPS TO FIND."

I THOUGHT I'D BE SAFE. I DIDN'T THINK THERE WAS ANYTHING ON HIM THAT COULD LINK HIM TO ME.

THE END

THE COLD CASE

CONNECTICUT TURNPIKE, FRIDAY, 16 JULY 1973, 12:00 PM.

21-YEAR-OLD CONCETTA 'PENNY' SERRA HAD TAKEN THE DAY OFF WORK.

AS SHE DROVE INTO THE CENTRE OF NEW HAVEN, SHE THOUGHT BACK TO EARLIER THAT MORNING...

...THAT'S NOT FAIR, IT'S MY TURN!

ROSE, SINCE WHEN DID WE TAKE TURNS USING THE BUICK?

YOU KNOW VERY WELL, WHEN DAD'S NOT HERE I'M IN CHARGE!

SINCE THEIR MUM'S DEATH IN 1963, PENNY HAD PLAYED A LARGE ROLE IN RAISING HER YOUNGER SISTER.

HER FATHER, JOHN SERRA, RAN A BUSY AUTO REPAIR SHOP.

SHE HAD DROPPED BY TO SEE HIM ON HER WAY OUT.

HER THOUGHTS TURNED TO HER ON-OFF BOYFRIEND, PHILIP DELEITO...

HMM...SHALL I STOP BY OR WILL HE BE TOO BUSY TODAY?

DELEITO WORKED THE LUNCH SHIFT AT HIS FAMILY'S DOWNTOWN RESTAURANT.

MAYBE I'LL HAVE LUNCH IN MACY'S AND DO SOME WINDOW SHOPPING INSTEAD.

AT 12:42 PM PENNY SERRA ENTERED TEMPLE STREET PARKING GARAGE.

1:20 PM.

SHE'S STILL WARM.

A YOUNG WOMAN STABBED TO DEATH IN A PUBLIC GARAGE IN BROAD DAYLIGHT.

THIS JUST DOESN'T HAPPEN HERE.

THERE SEEMS TO BE A BLOOD TRAIL HERE, LEADING DOWN.

LEVEL 8, SECTION A.

I SAW BLOOD ON THE STAIR RAILING, SO WE'LL NEED TAPE-LIFTS OF THAT.

PLATE IS REGISTERED TO A JOHN SERRA OF HUNTINGTON AVENUE.

WE FOUND THIS AUTOMOBILE...

FOUND A WALLET CONTAINING $14.75 TOGETHER WITH A DRIVER'S LICENCE FOR CONCETTA SERRA.

CONNECTICUT STATE
DRIVER LICENSE

THERE'S BLOOD ALL OVER THE STEERING COLUMN, BUT NO SIGN OF THE KEYS.

WE'LL NEED THE EVIDENCE GUYS TO DO A REAL THOROUGH JOB ON THIS ONE...

BEHIND THE DRIVER'S SEAT EVIDENCE TECHNICIANS FIND A RAG...

...LIKE THE KIND USED IN AUTO SHOPS.

WE GOT SOME GOOD LATENTS* FROM THIS.

*LATENT FINGERPRINTS - FINGERPRINTS THAT AREN'T VISIBLE UNTIL REVEALED THROUGH A PROCESS.

33

AFTER HE TAKES PART IN A POLICE LINEUP, SERRA'S BOYFRIEND, DELEITO, IS EXCLUDED FROM THE INVESTIGATION.

THAT RULES OUT A CRIME OF PASSION.

MOST LIKELY A STRANGER CRIME, THEN.

WITH LITTLE ELSE TO GO ON, THEY FOCUS ON THE PHYSICAL EVIDENCE...

...UNIDENTIIFED PRINTS ON THE TISSUE BOX, A BLOODIED, PAINT-STAINED HANDKERCHIEF AND A DISCARDED AUTO SHOP RAG.

HOWEVER, THERE ARE MORE THAN 2,500 AUTO REPAIR SHOPS IN THE NEW HAVEN AREA ALONE.

ANOTHER STRIKEOUT - THIS IS GOING TO TAKE MONTHS, IF NOT YEARS!

THE FINGERPRINTS REMAIN UNMATCHED AND DESPITE ALL THE BLOOD EVIDENCE...

...ALL WE KNOW IS THAT THE VICTIM HAD TYPE A BLOOD AND THE ASSAILANT'S, FOUND IN THE GARAGE AND THE CAR, IS TYPE O.

DESPITE THEIR BEST EFFORTS, THE SERRA CASE IS BEGINNING TO APPEAR **UNSOLVABLE**.

HUNTINGTON AVENUE, NEW HAVEN, JULY 1974.

NEW HAVEN REGISTER, CLASSIFIED SECTION, HOW MAY I HELP?

I'D LIKE TO PLACE AN ADVERTISEMENT PLEASE. TEXT AS FOLLOWS...

PENNY SERRA, MURDERED IN TEMPLE STREET GARAGE, DOWNTOWN NEW HAVEN, ON 16 JULY 1973. TO DATE, KILLER STILL IN NEW HAVEN AREA, PAID FOR BY...

...JOHN SERRA.

FOR THE NEXT 25 YEARS, JOHN SERRA CONTINUES TO PLACE REGULAR ADS IN THE NEW HAVEN REGISTER, KEEPING THE CASE IN THE PUBLIC EYE.

IN 1984, ANTHONY GOLINO, A PAST STUDENT AT PENNY SERRA'S HIGH SCHOOL, IS ARRESTED.

THE CHARGES ARE DROPPED WHEN POLICE DISCOVER HE HAS **THE WRONG BLOOD TYPE.**

PENNY SERRA
MURDERED IN TEMPLE

IN 1987, ADVANCES IN SCIENCE BRING THE CONNECTICUT STATE POLICE FORENSICS LAB INTO BEING.

IN EARLY 1988 THE SERRA COLD CASE IS REASSIGNED TO DR HENRY C. LEE AND HIS TEAM AT THE LAB.

METICULOUS RECORDS HAVE BEEN KEPT, THE EVIDENCE CAREFULLY LOGGED AND STORED.

LEE ORDERS A RECONSTRUCTION OF THE CRIME AND A **RE-EXAMINATION** OF THE FORENSIC EVIDENCE.

SEPTEMBER 1989, TEMPLE STREET GARAGE, NEW HAVEN...

...WE NOW HAVE A MUCH CLEARER PICTURE OF THE MURDERER'S MOVEMENTS ON THAT DAY.

I'M ALSO HOPEFUL THAT THE RECENT ADVANCES IN FINGERPRINT AND DNA TECHNOLOGY WILL SOMEDAY HELP US TO SOLVE THIS MURDER.

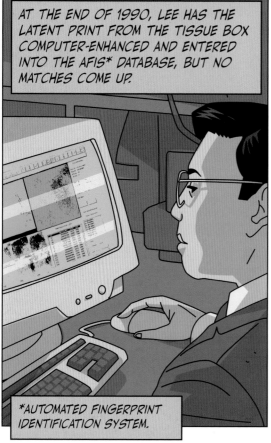

AT THE END OF 1990, LEE HAS THE LATENT PRINT FROM THE TISSUE BOX COMPUTER-ENHANCED AND ENTERED INTO THE AFIS* DATABASE, BUT NO MATCHES COME UP.

*AUTOMATED FINGERPRINT IDENTIFICATION SYSTEM.

1994, WATERBURY HOSPITAL, NEW HAVEN COUNTY.

HE BEAT YOU?

UH-HUH.

DO YOU WANT US TO CALL THE POLICE?

YES.

THE WOMAN'S FIANCÉ, EDWARD GRANT, IS ARRESTED AND FINGERPRINTED, ALTHOUGH THE CHARGES ARE LATER DROPPED.

HOLD STILL, PLEASE.

AT A CONNECTICUT/RHODE ISLAND FINGERPRINT DATABASE IN 1997...

MATCH!

subject: Edward R. Grant
left thumbprint
matched with a partial from
Concetta Serra murder case

COLD CASE SQUAD, CONNECTICUT STATE POLICE DEPARTMENT...

HE'S AN AUTO REPAIR WORKER WITH A HISTORY OF VIOLENCE AGAINST WOMEN!

WHAT ARE WE WAITING FOR? LET'S SEE HIM.

I HAVE NO IDEA HOW MY FINGERPRINT COULD HAVE GOTTEN IN THERE.

THERE'S A REALLY EASY WAY YOU COULD RULE YOURSELF OUT OF THIS ENTIRE INVESTIGATION.

ALL YOU NEED TO DO IS GIVE US A SAMPLE OF **BLOOD**.

NO, I THINK I NEED TO SPEAK TO A LAWYER NOW.

DETECTIVES GET A WARRANT FOR THE BLOOD SAMPLE.

WHEN GRANT'S DNA IS ANALYSED AND COMPARED AGAINST DNA FROM THE TYPE OF BLOOD RETRIEVED AT THE SCENE...

IT'S A MATCH!

LATER, DR LEE TALKS ABOUT THE CRIME SCENE...

THE INCIDENT BEGAN WHEN EDWARD GRANT THREATENED OR ATTACKED MISS SERRA AS SHE PARKED HER CAR ON THE NINTH FLOOR.

↑TO LEVEL 10

"DURING THE STRUGGLE, MR GRANT WAS WOUNDED IN HIS LEFT HAND. MISS SERRA THEN RAN TO THE TENTH FLOOR, WITH MR GRANT IN PURSUIT."

"TRAPPED IN THE BLIND STAIRWELL SHE HAD NOWHERE TO GO."

"PENNY SERRA DIED IN LESS THAN 90 SECONDS."

"STILL BLEEDING, GRANT DROVE THE BUICK TO THE EIGHTH LEVEL, REACHING BEHIND THE SEAT FOR TISSUES TO STAUNCH HIS WOUND."

THE ACT OF TURNING OVER THE TISSUE BOX LEFT BEHIND THE LATENT PRINT YOU CAN SEE ON THE SCREEN.

ALTHOUGH IT TAKES THE JURY FOUR DAYS, THEY REACH A GUILTY VERDICT.

AT THE SENTENCING THE DEFENDANT SPEAKS...

I DIDN'T *MURDER* PENNY SERRA, BUT I DO FEEL SORRY FOR ALL THE SUFFERING THE FAMILY HAS ENDURED.

JUDGE BLUE IS PRESIDING...

ALL THE PERFUMES OF ARABIA WILL NOT SWEETEN YOUR BLOODSTAINED HANDS! YOU WILL SERVE 20 TO LIFE.

ROSEMARY SERRA HAS THE FINAL SAY...

IF YOU HAD COME FORWARD 29 YEARS AGO, MAYBE I WOULD NOT HAVE HAD TO LOOK INTO MY FATHER'S HAUNTED EYES.

YOU TURNED TIME INTO OUR **ENEMY**.

THE END

OTHER FAMOUS CASES

Here are some other celebrated cases that relied on forensic trace evidence to help solve a crime.

THE FRANCISCA ROJAS CASE

In 1891 in Argentina, an official, Juan Vucetich, set up a basic fingerprint classification system. The following year two children were found at home battered to death. The mother, Francisca Rojas, accused a neighbour, Pedro Ramon Velasquez, of being the killer. Velasquez admitted he once threatened her but even under torture said he was innocent. Police Chief Eduardo Alvarez suspected Francisca. Examining the murder scene closely, he found a bloody thumbprint.

Comparision with Francisca's thumbprint proved it was hers and she'd already denied touching the bodies. Confronted with the evidence, she confessed she had killed her children to be free to marry a much younger man. Rojas was the first person found guilty by fingerprint evidence.

THE MAIL TRAIN MURDERS

Following a botched train robbery in 1923 in Oregon, a local mechanic was arrested for the murder of three railroad employees. The evidence, a pair of grease-stained overalls found at the scene, was given to forensics expert Professor Oscar Heinrich. He told the police that they had the wrong man. Trace evidence on the overalls had shown that the assailant was a brown-haired, left-handed lumberjack, 21 to 25 years old, 1.78 metres tall and of meticulous habits.

The grease was fir pitch, and a brown hair was caught in a buttonhole. Precise nail clippings were in the right-hand pocket. The information helped catch the perpetrator a month later.

THE PITCHFORK MURDER CASE

Leicester, United Kingdom, 1987. An unsolved murder case involving separate assaults on two girls, one in 1983 and one in 1986, less than a kilometre apart was taxing the police.

A 17-year-old youth had been arrested on flimsy evidence. Needing proof, detectives had sent a sample of his saliva to the lab of Dr Alec Jeffreys at Leicester University. Jeffreys had developed a new identification test using DNA. However, when the youth's DNA profile was compared with the profile based on evidence collected from the bodies, it did not match.

In desperation the police randomly tested 5,000 males in the local area, again with no result. The case was looking unsolvable when someone overheard a man bragging about fooling the police by supplying a false blood sample for his friend. The friend, Colin Pitchfork, was quickly arrested.

By the time his positive lab match came back he had confessed to the crimes. Pitchfork was the first person found guilty of homicide through DNA fingerprinting.

FELINE WITNESS

The first time animal DNA was used to solve a crime was in Canada in 1994. The body of a missing 32-year-old, Shirley Duguay, was found on Prince Edward Island. Her estranged common-law husband, Doug Beamish, was the prime suspect. A bloodstained jacket suspected of being his had been found near the body, but no family members would testify that he owned it.

White hairs on the jacket were carefully examined and turned out to belong to a cat. Mounties recalled that a white cat named Snowball lived at Beamish's parents' house. They had Snowball's blood tested and found his DNA matched the hair's. Beamish was convicted of second-degree murder.

GLOSSARY

analysis Detailed examination of the parts that make up a piece of evidence.

assailant A person who attacks another.

circumstantial Evidence that points indirectly to a person's guilt, but does not prove it.

classify To arrange fingerprints into groups based on shared patterns.

conscript One who is drafted, or forced, to join a group.

comparison The comparing of one fingerprint with another.

confession A written or oral statement, acknowledging guilt.

dactyloscopy The science of comparing fingerprints to make an identification.

enhancement Improvement of the quality of a partial fingerprint.

meticulous To be extremely careful and precise.

microscopy The use of a microscope for analysis.

New Scotland Yard Headquarters of the Greater London Metropolitan Police Force.

partial print An incomplete or smudged fingerprint.

post-mortem A medical examination of a dead body.

precise Highly accurate.

principle A basic truth.

remand To return to custody or detention.

serology Scientific study of blood.

spectroscope A machine for producing and analysing the light given off by different materials.

staunch Stop the flow of.

tape-lift A technique used to preserve and transport a sample for later microscopy.

testify To make a declaration of truth under oath.

toxins Natural and human-made poisons that cause disease.

warrant A writ issued by a judge, authorising an officer to make a search, a seizure, or an arrest.

FOR MORE INFORMATION

ORGANISATIONS

International Crime Scene Investigators Association
PMB 385
15774 S. LaGrange Road
Orland Park, IL 60462
USA
(708) 460-8082
Website: http://www.icsia.org

The FBI Academy
Forensic Science Research & Training Center
Hoover Road
Quantico, VA 22135
USA
(703) 632 1000
Website: http://www.fbi.gov

FOR FURTHER READING

Baden, Michael M. *Dead Reckoning: the New Science of Catching Killers.* London: Arrow Books Ltd, 2002.

Davis, Barbara. *In the Laboratory (Crime Scene Science).* Tunbridge Wells: Ticktock Media Ltd, 2007.

Fridell, Ron. *DNA Fingerprinting: The Ultimate Identity.* Oxford: Scholastic, 2001.

Prokos, Anna. *Killer Wallpaper: True Confessions of Deadly Poisonings* (24/7: Science Behind the Scenes: Forensic Files). Danbury, CT: Children's Press, 2007.

Platt, Richard. *Crime Scene: The Ultimate Guide to Forensic Science.* London: Dorling Kindersley, 2006

INDEX